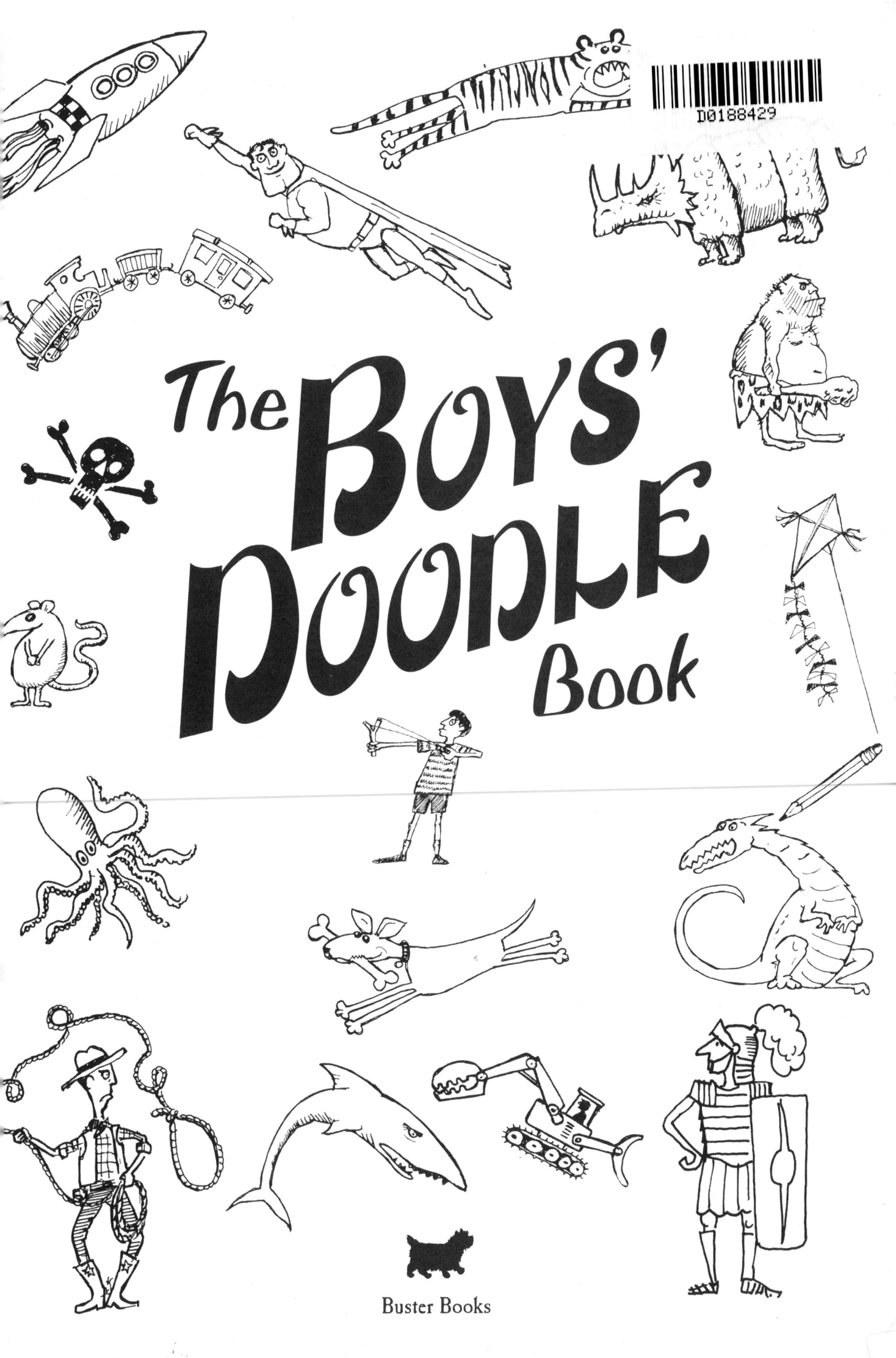

The Boys' Doodle Book

Buster Books

Illustrated by Andrew Pinder

First published in Great Britain in 2008 by Buster Books,
an imprint of Michael O'Mara Books Limited,
9 Lion Yard, Tremadoc Road,
London SW4 7NQ

A CIP catalogue record for this book is available from the British Library.

ISBN: 978-1-906082-23-9

2 4 6 8 10 9 7 5 3

Printed and bound in China by Imago

www.mombooks.com/busterbooks

Invent a robot.

Alien invasion!

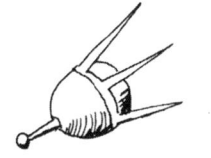

If only I had feet!

Make their shields scary.

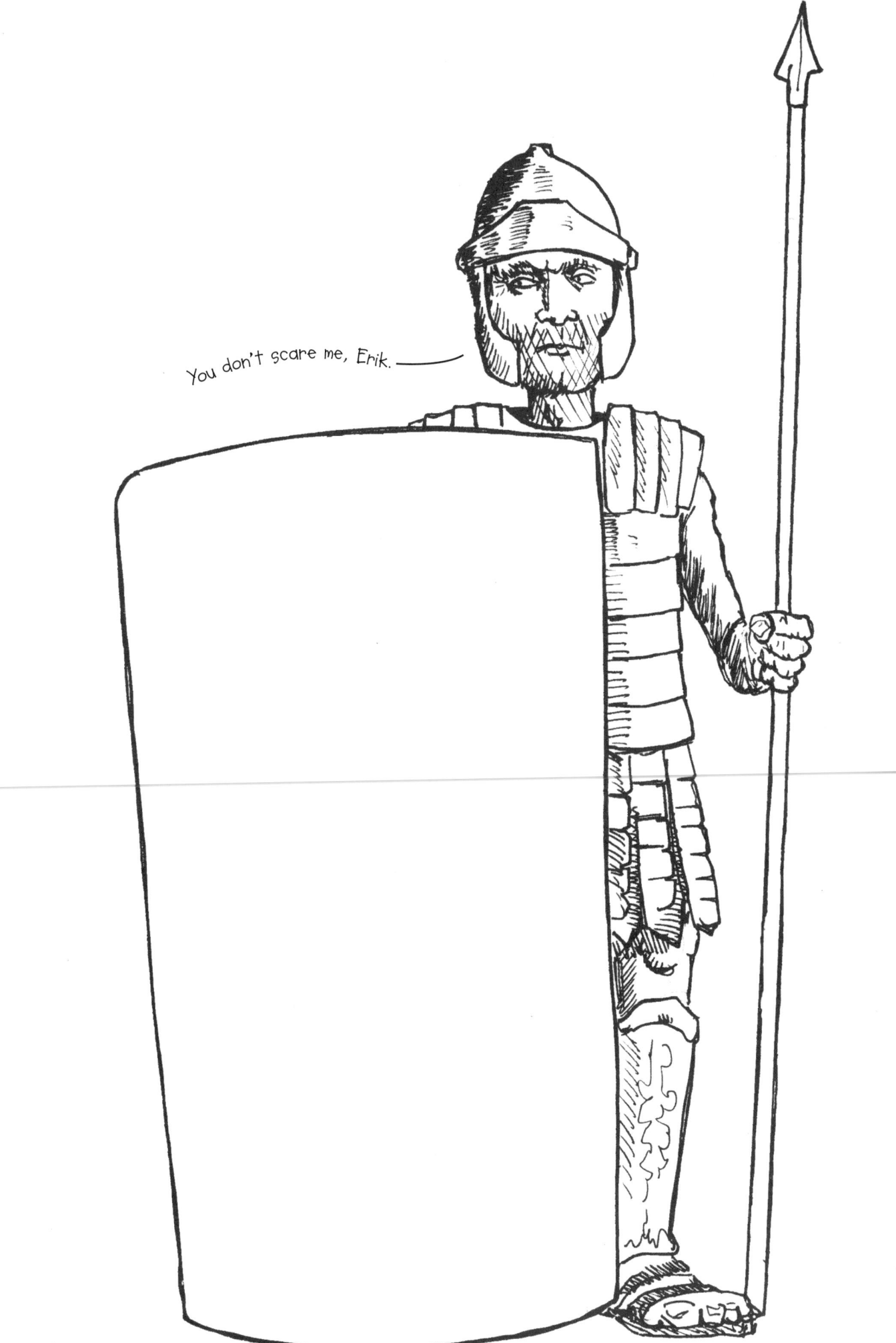

Add Wild Bill's bucking bronco.

Whoops!

Help! Get me out of here.

Mmmm, lunch.

Shiver m'timbers – what's in the chest?

— Ooh, shiny!

Who is your hero?

What is nibbling his toes?

Finish the castle.

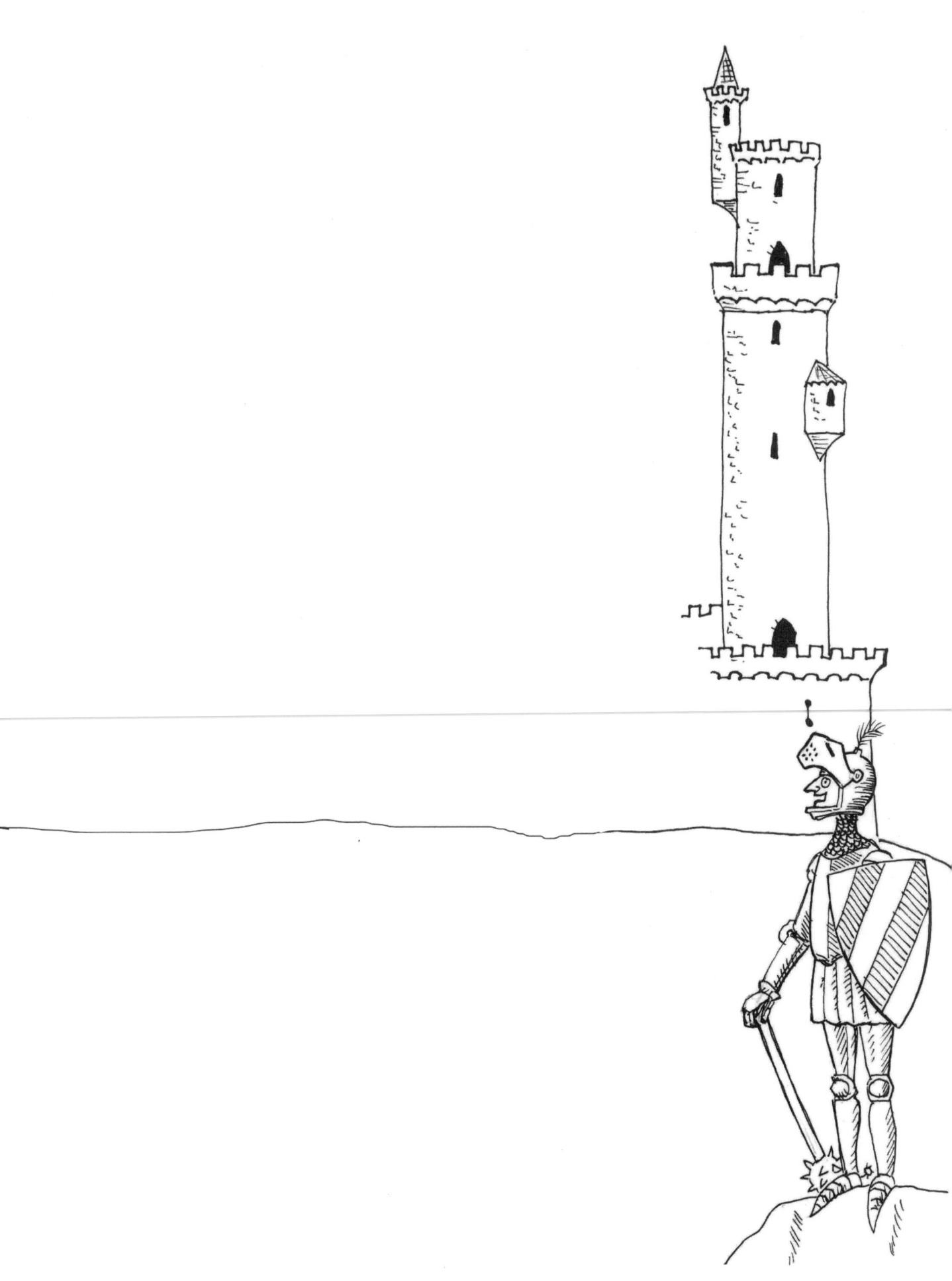

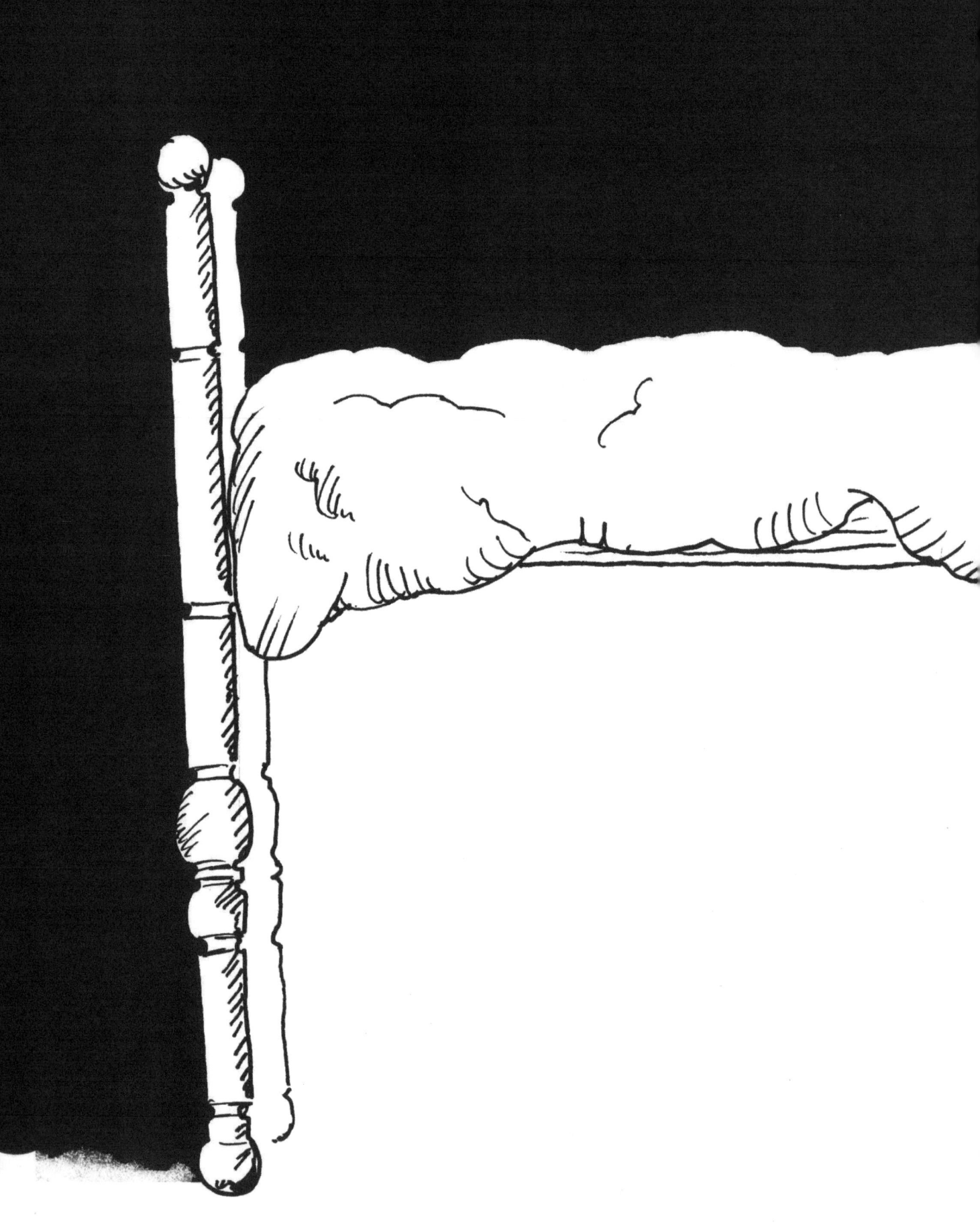

What's under the bed?

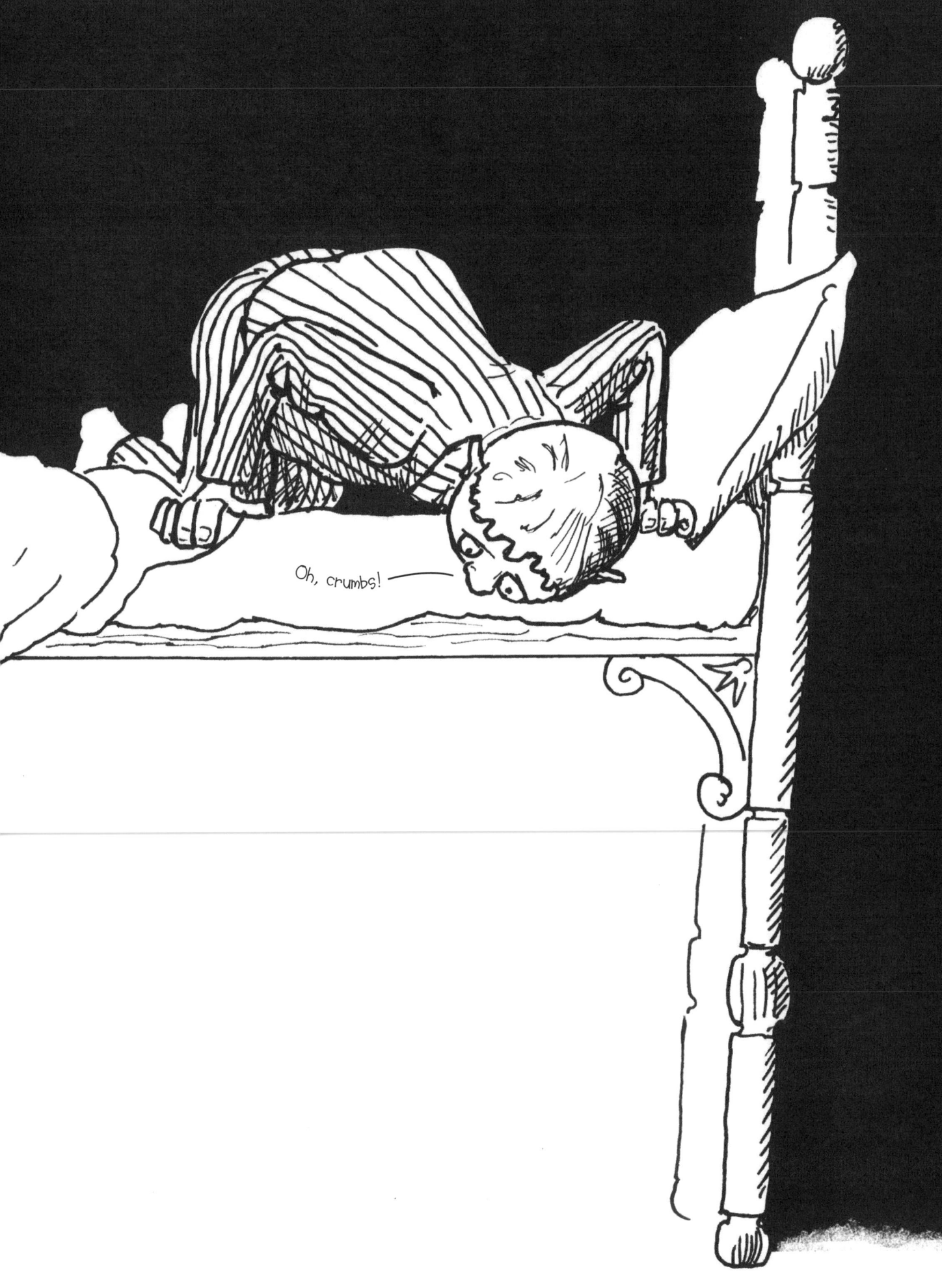

Wanted
DEAD OR ALIVE

ONE-EYED JAKE
$1000
REWARD

Draw Dr Frankenstein's monster.

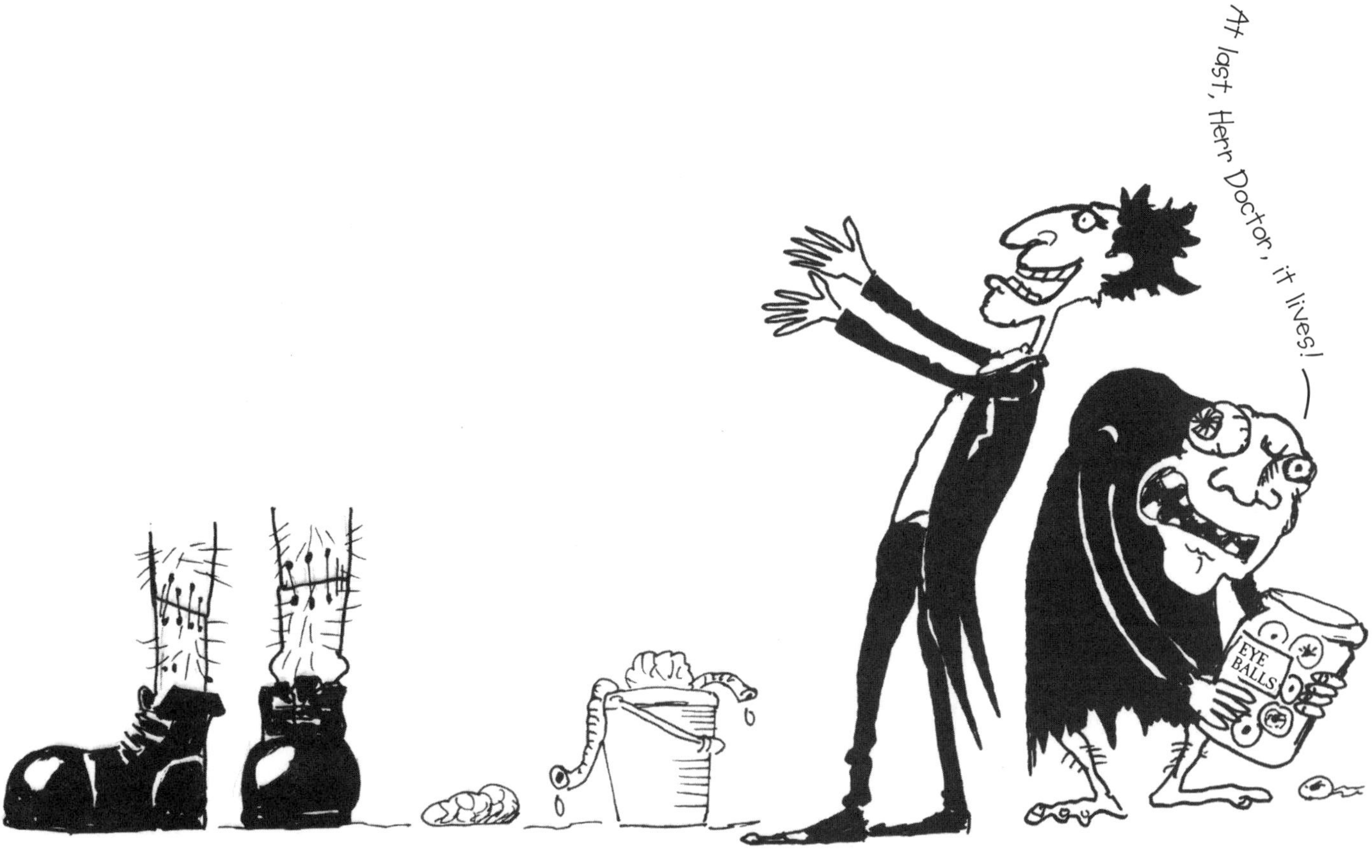
At last, Herr Doctor, it lives!
EYE BALLS

What's down there?

Design their superhero costumes.

What spooked him?

What's he laughing at?

What are the lions hunting?

What is hunting the lions?

What did he lasso?

Ship ahoy!

Sketch in some slimy specimens.

Build them a space city . . .

ᛩ*^(§§@!

. . . and their dogs a space kennel.

Yuk!

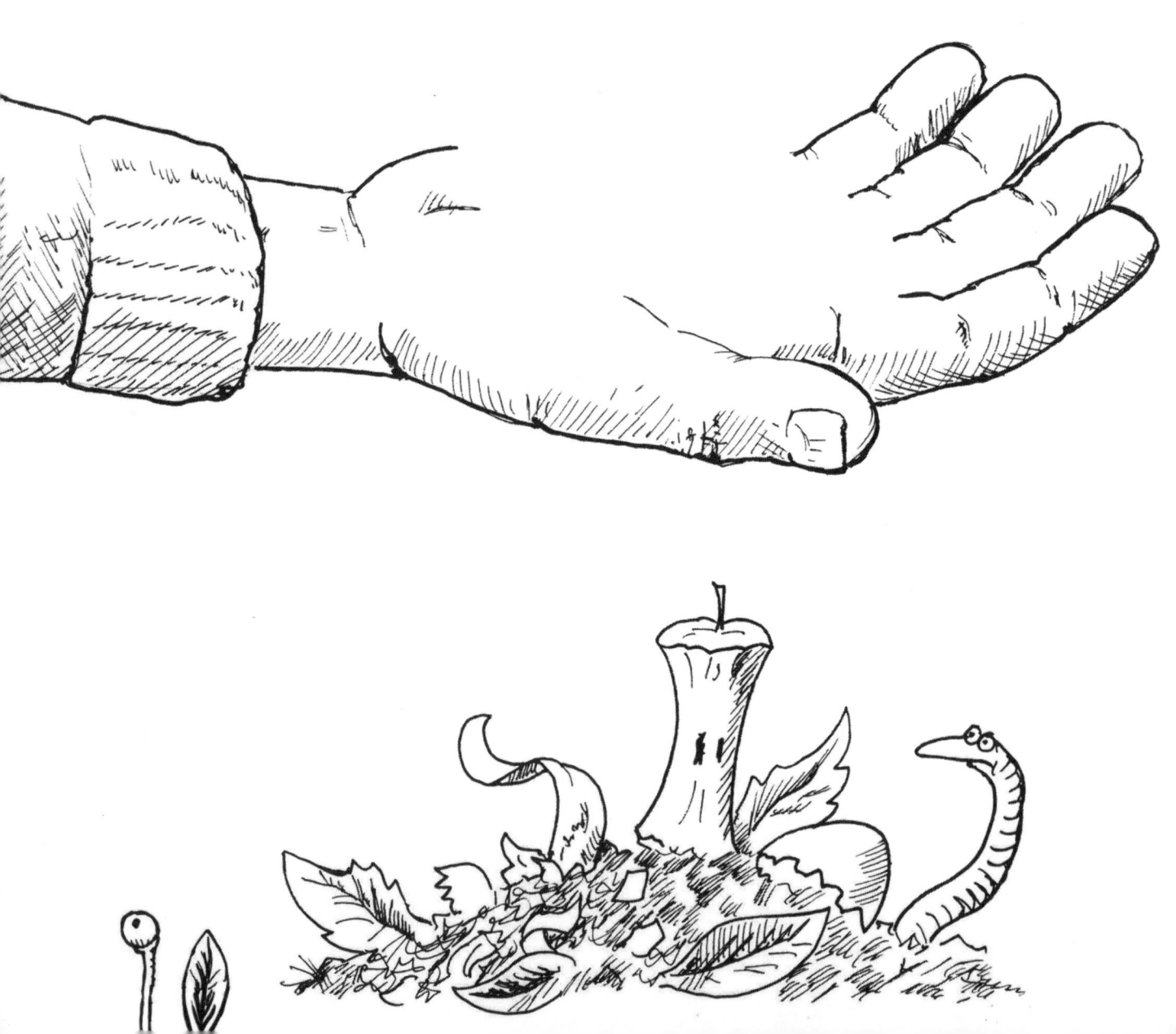

Who is hunting for presents?

Finish the toboggan run.

What is his excuse?

He shoots . . . he scores!

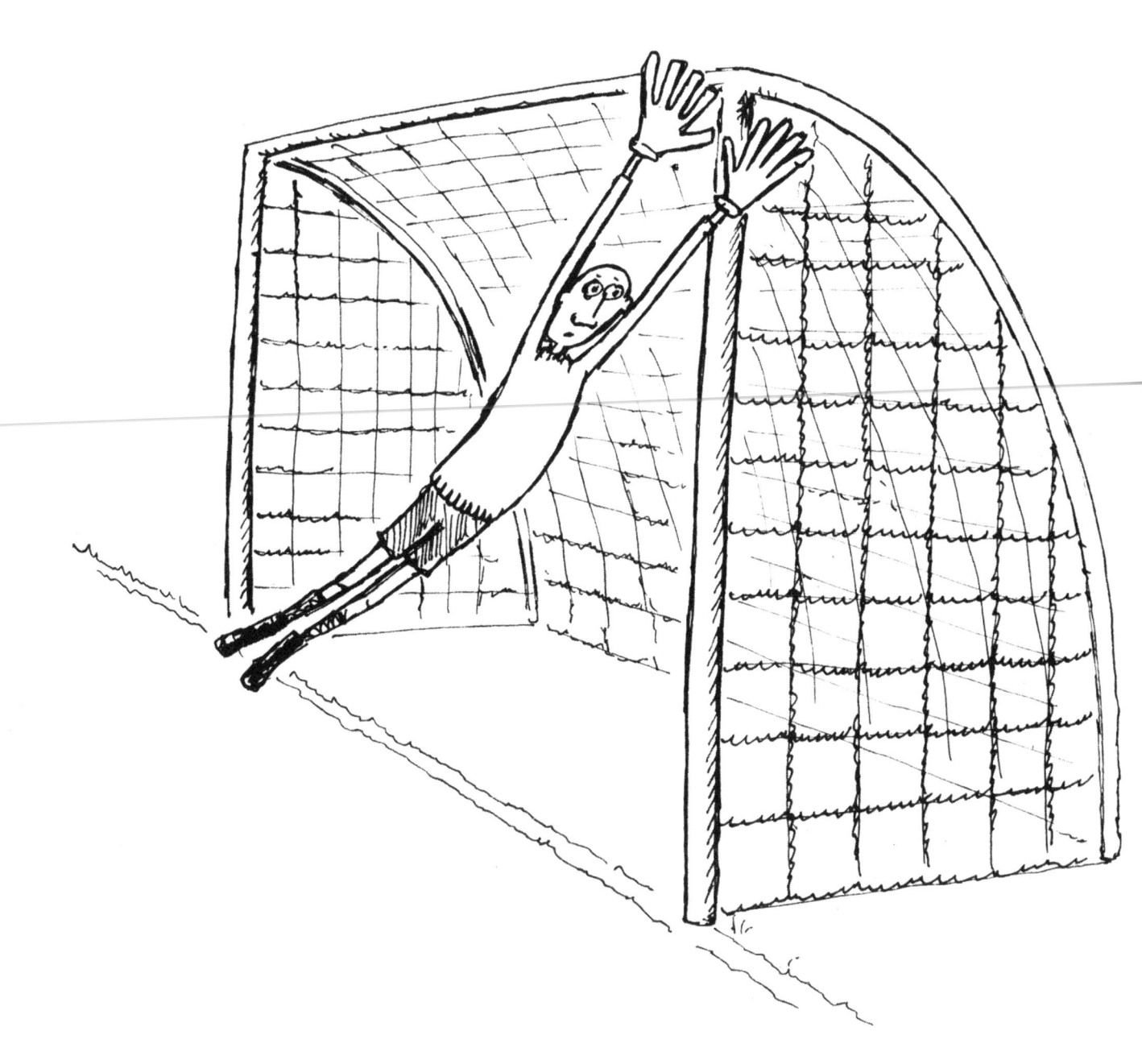

Who is watching Coco the Clown?

Abracadabra!

Draw a dreadful dragon.

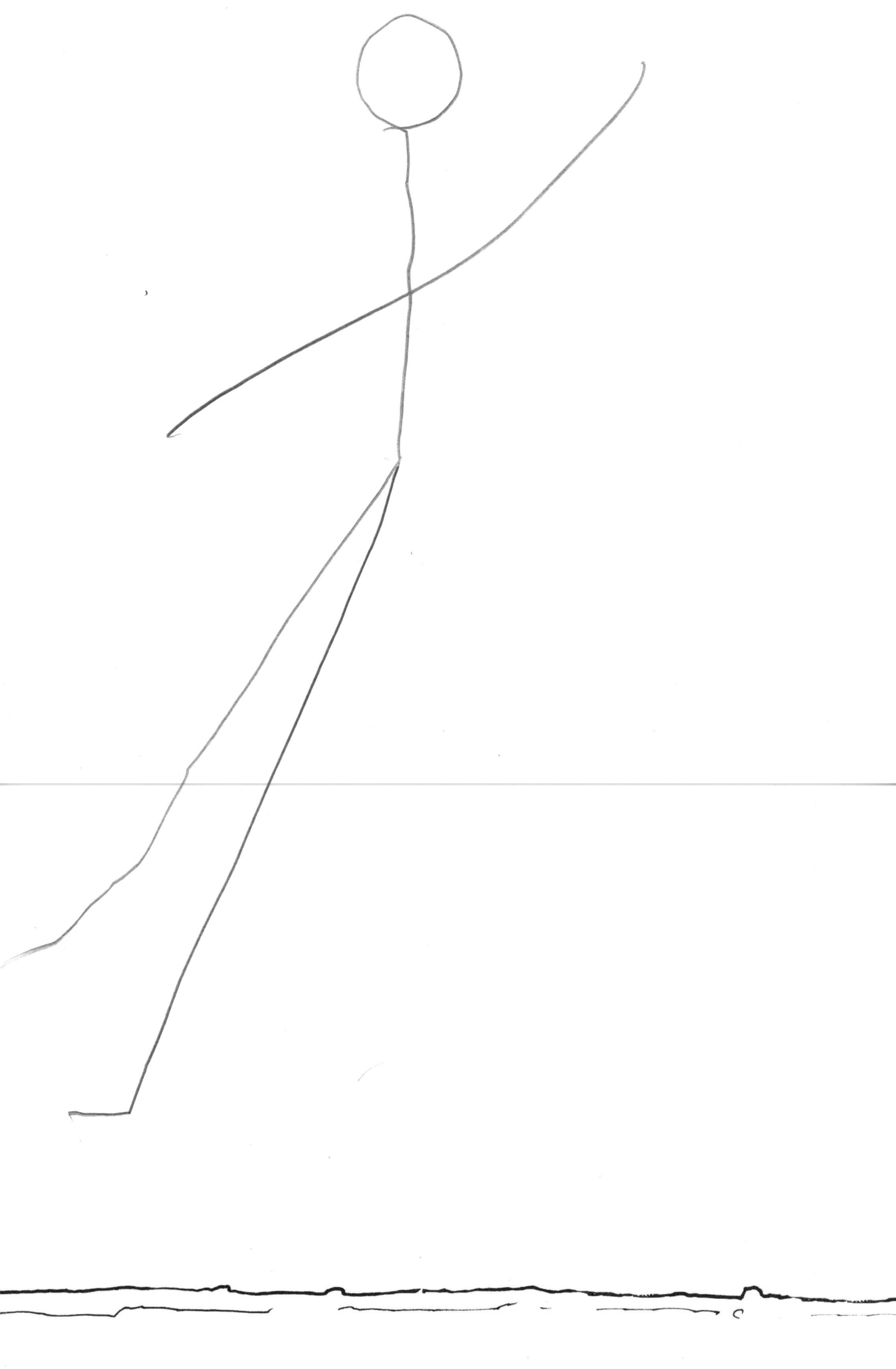

What did he do?

What hatched from the dino-eggs?

Draw him some armour.

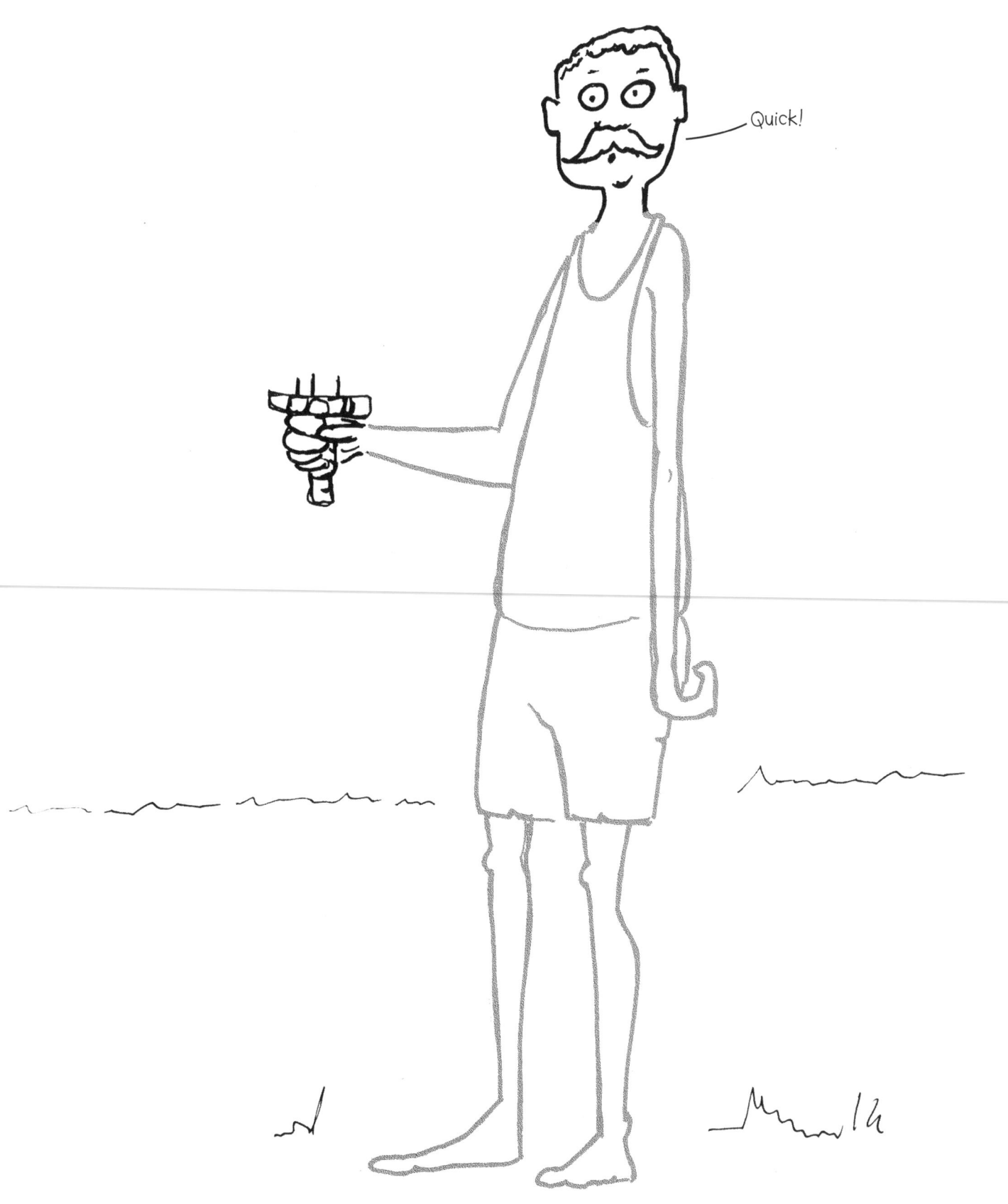

Design an incredible flying machine.

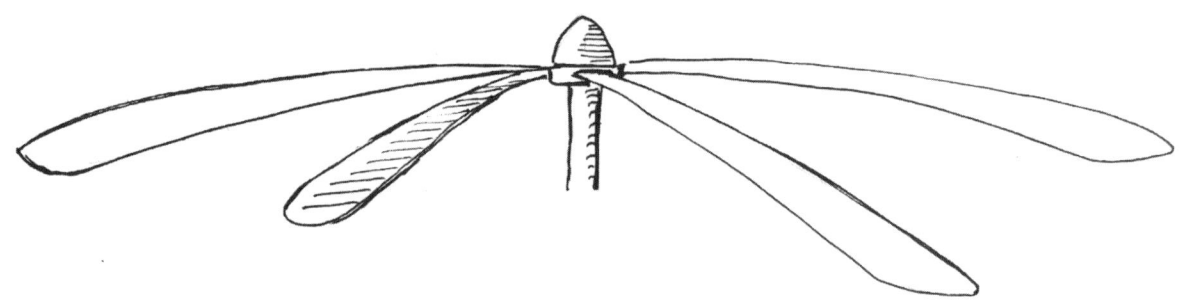

But will it fly?

Surf's up!

What's in the cave?

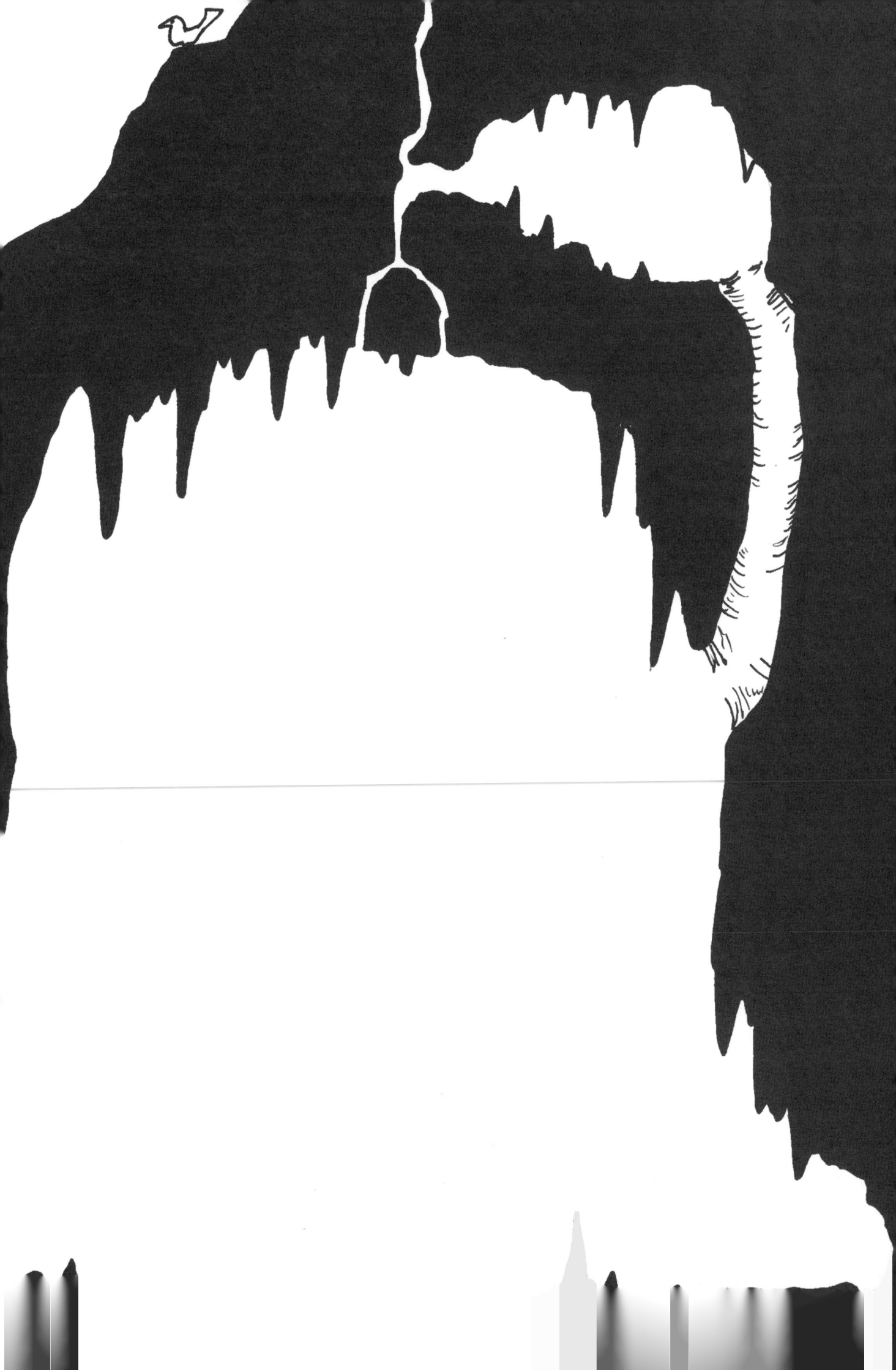

Finish the treasure map.

Make his hair look cool.

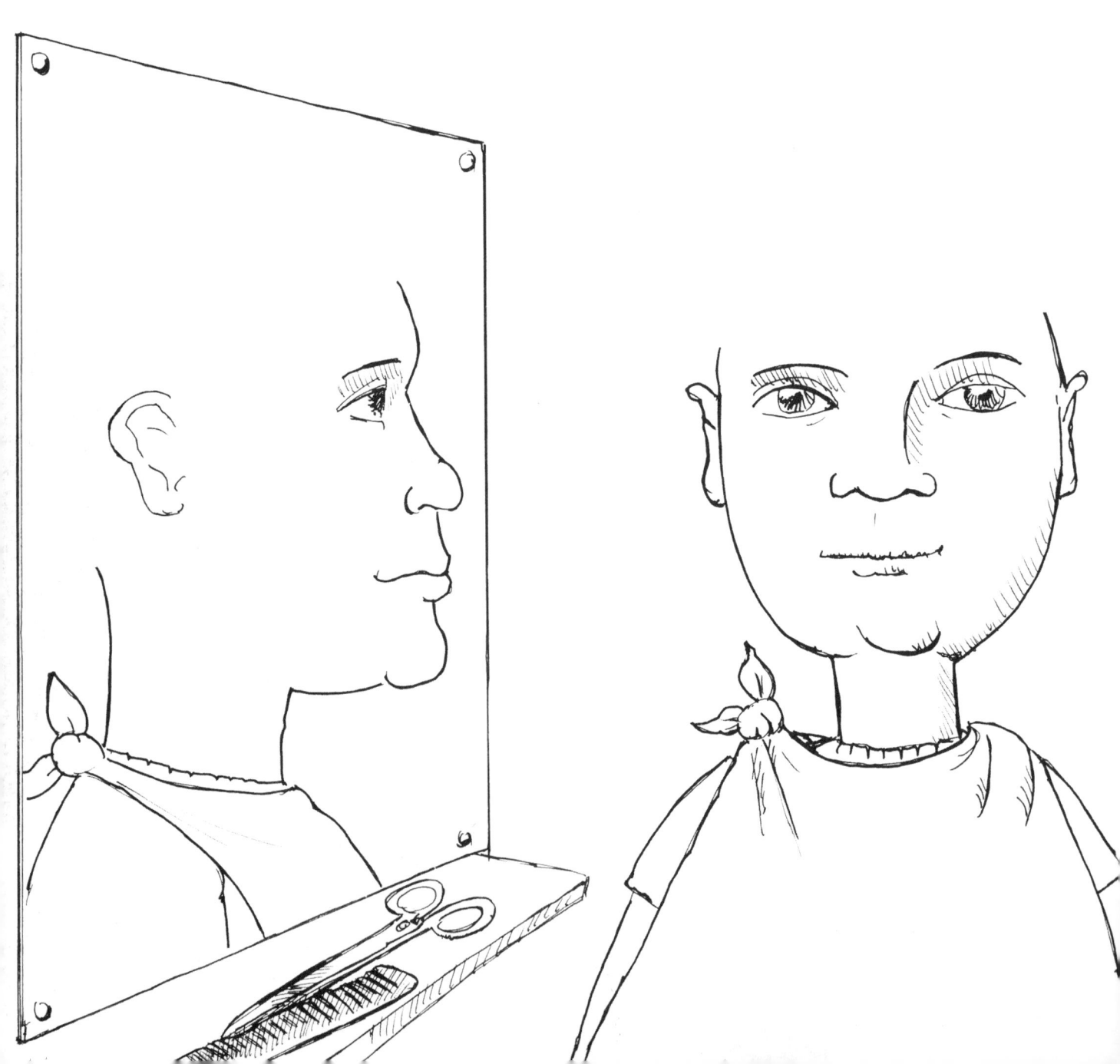

Sweet dreams . . .

Who is sitting on the eggs?

What's happening in the castle?

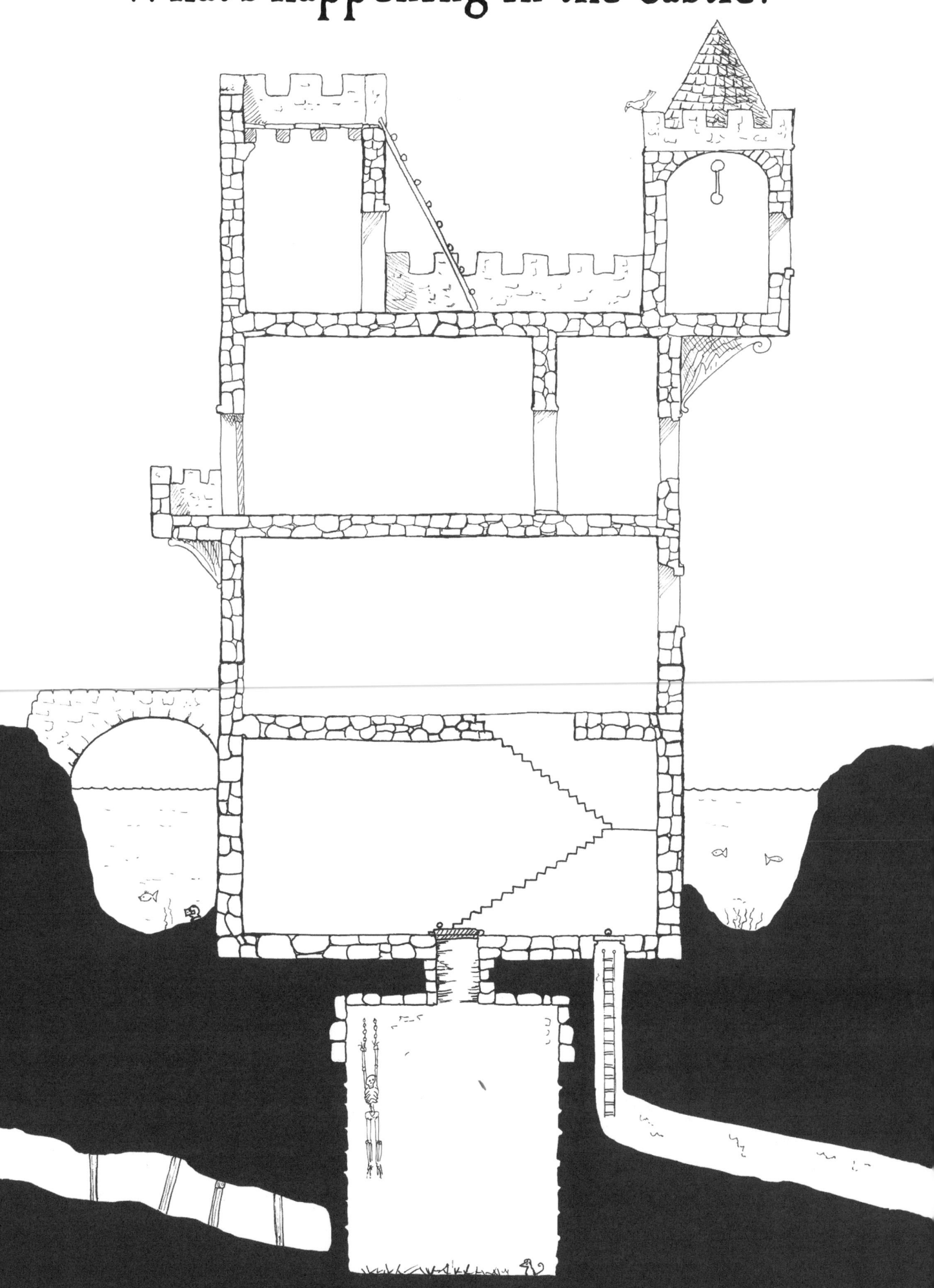

My perfect holiday . . .

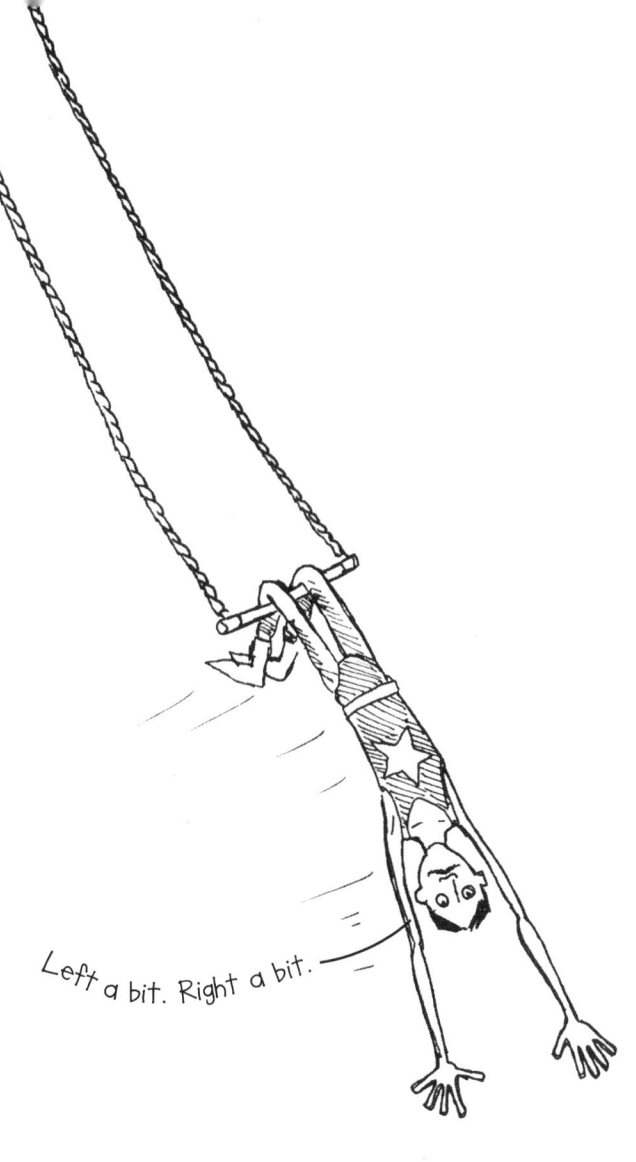

Left a bit. Right a bit.

Complete the circus trick.

Launch the rocket.

Complete the monster.

What did these ants build?

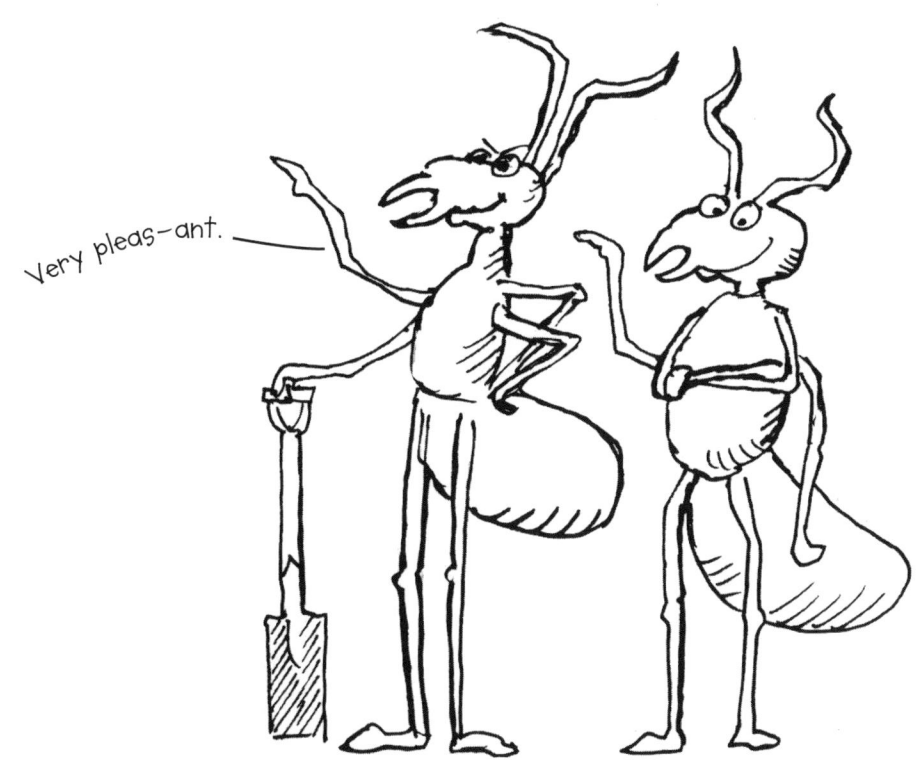

Very pleas—ant.

Construct a cool tree house.

Who is visiting the haunted house?

Fix the bridge and save the people.

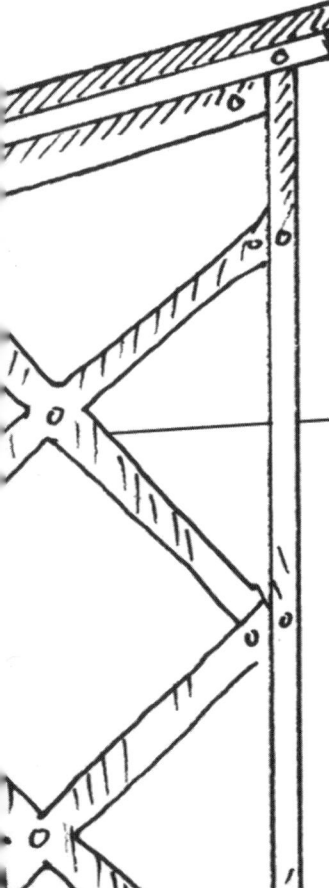

What is he jumping over?

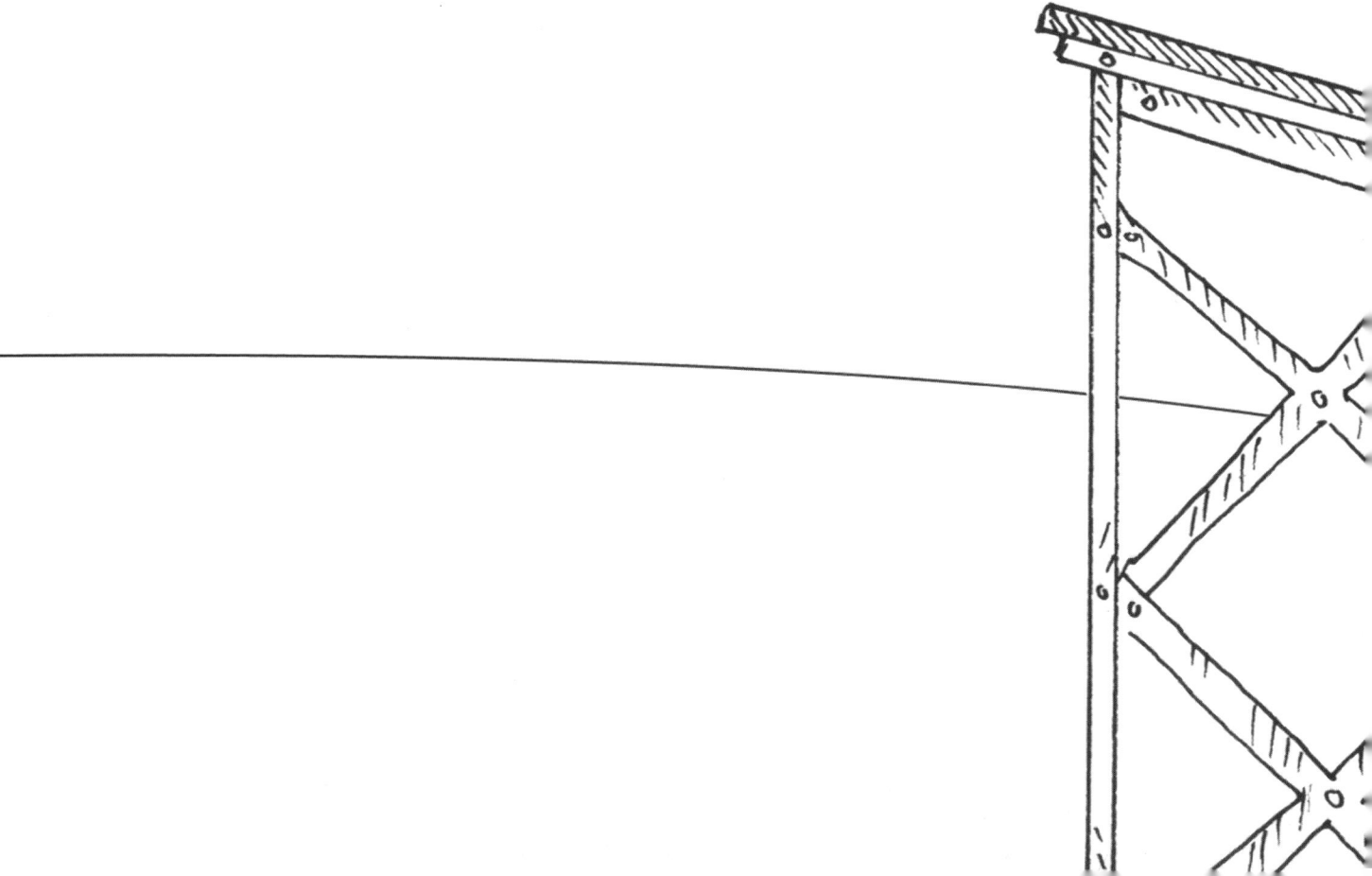

What is twisting in the tornado?

Design a great gadget.

What went bang in the night?

Draw their dinner . . .

But I'm a vegetarian.

. . . and their pudding.

Just a small slice for me.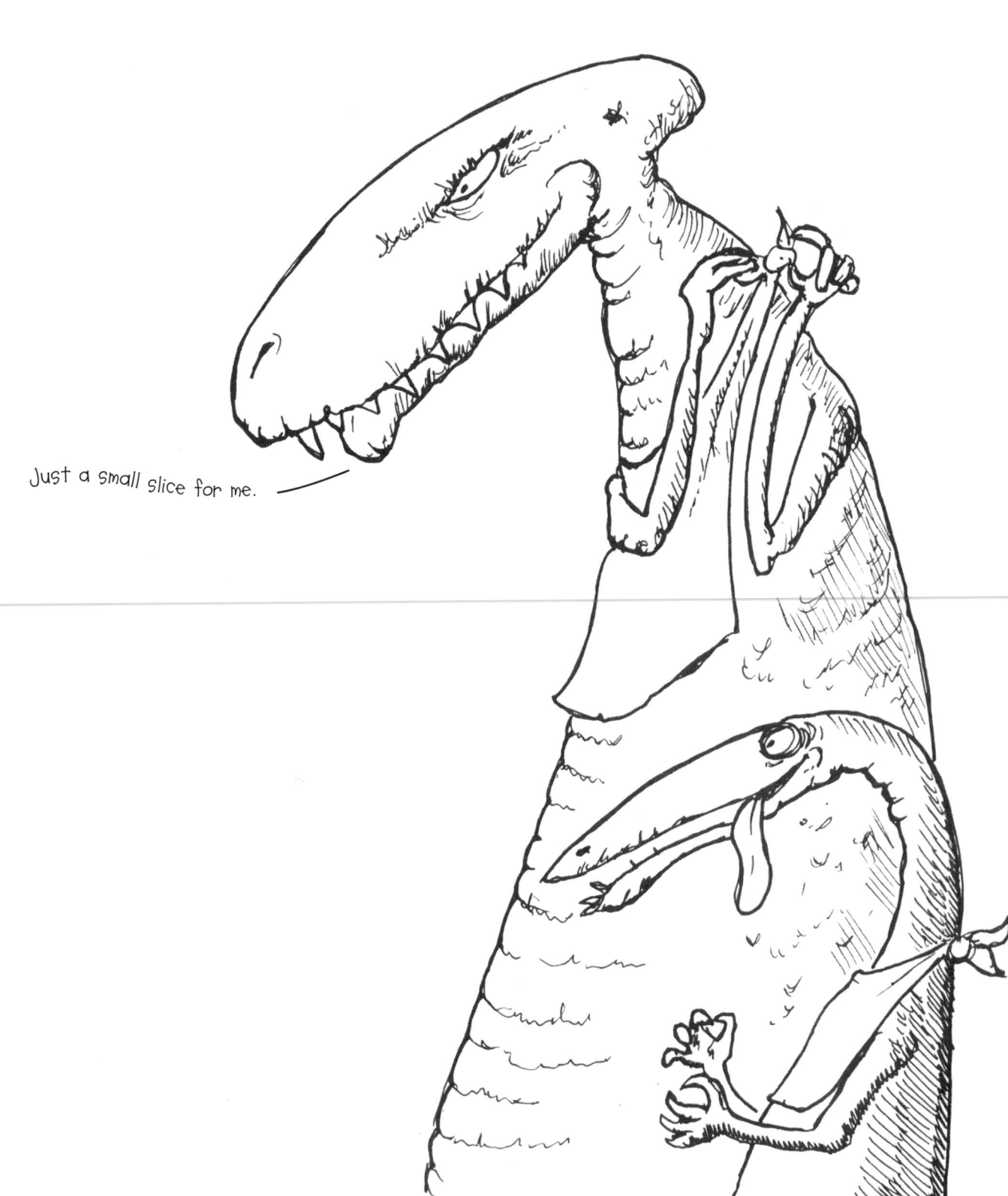

What a weird alien.

Draw his planet.

Oh no! A supervillain.

Who will save us?

What are his evil powers?

Bring a superhero to the rescue.

Save us super one...

What are his super powers?

Who is crossing the river . . .

. . . and how?

What scared him?

Yikes!

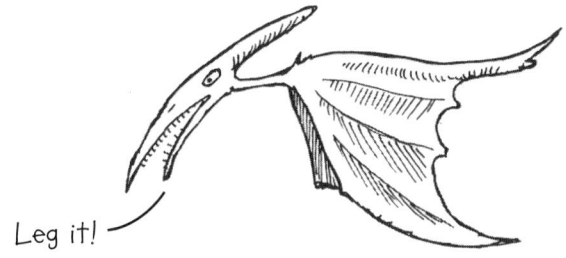

Leg it!

What is he lifting?

Where are they visiting?

Design a monster truck.

Cool!

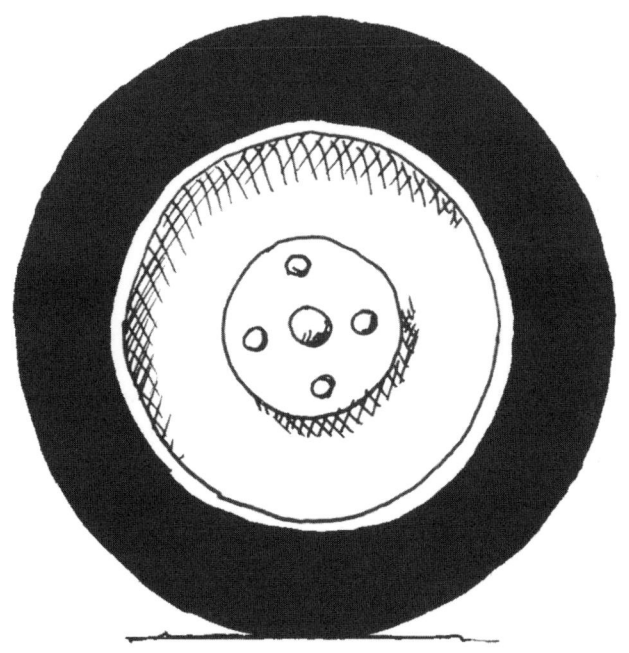

Captain Jack.

No comment.

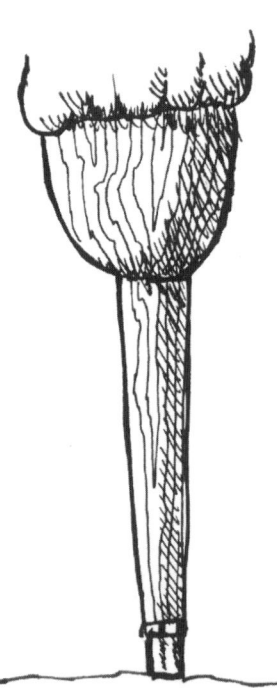

What is eating the bait?

Why is the caveman fleeing?

Finish the balls.

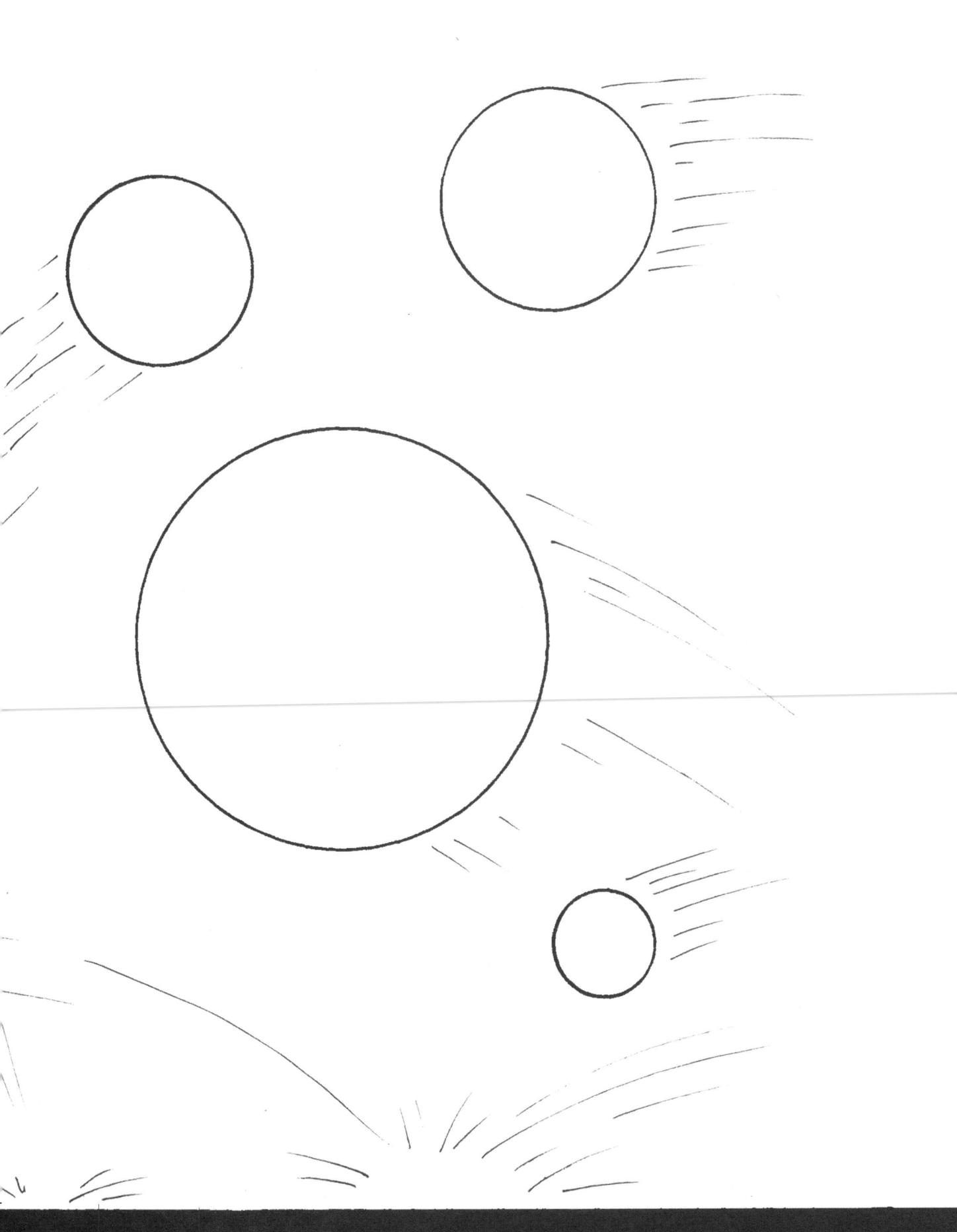

Complete the Viking fleet.

What's cooking?

Draw the fire brigade . . .

Did you turn the oven off?

... putting out the fire.

Stop the thief.

What is happening in the big top?

What's in the haunted mine?

Can you stop the stampede?

Disguise the spy.

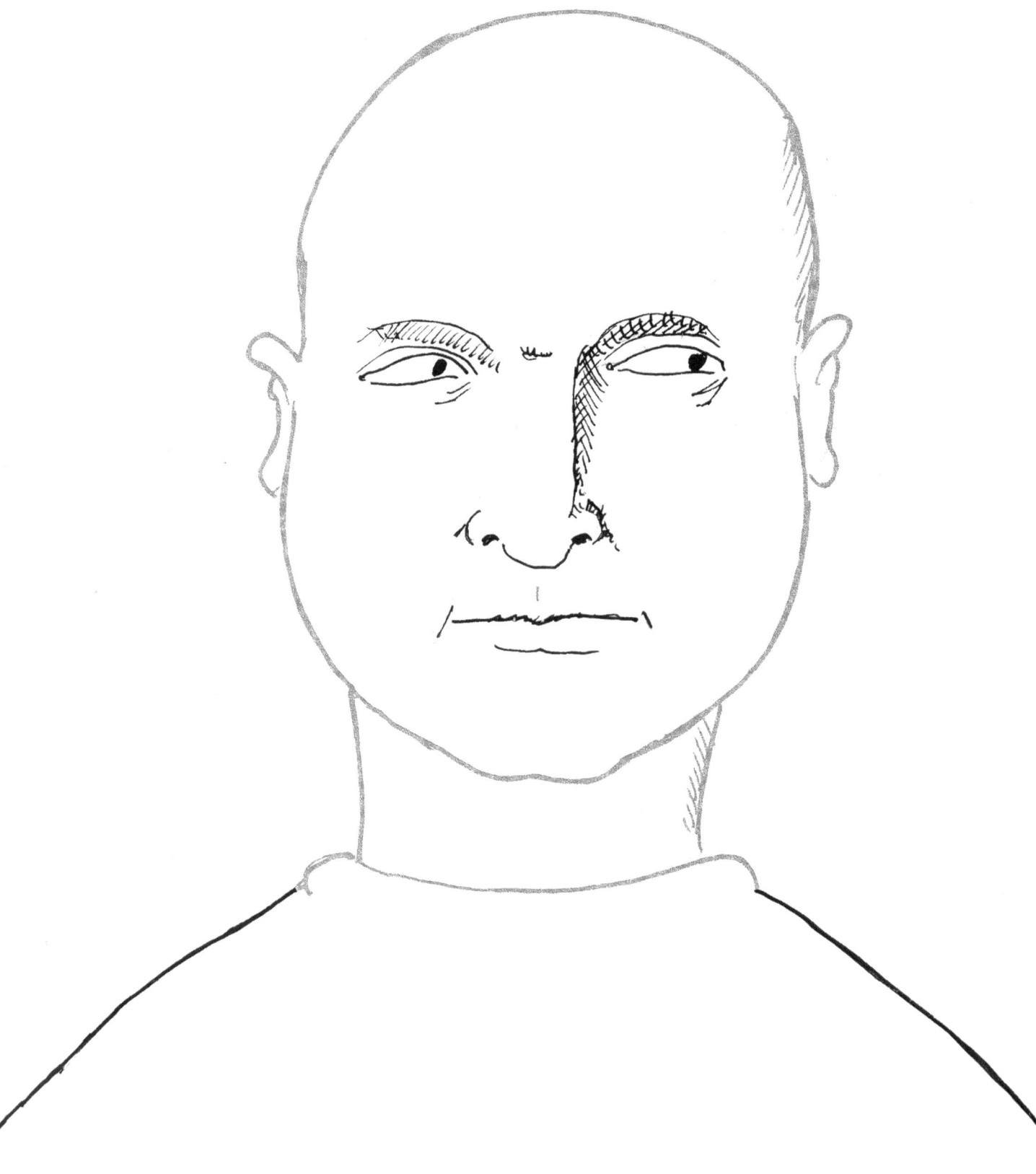

Top a brilliant pizza for yourself . . .

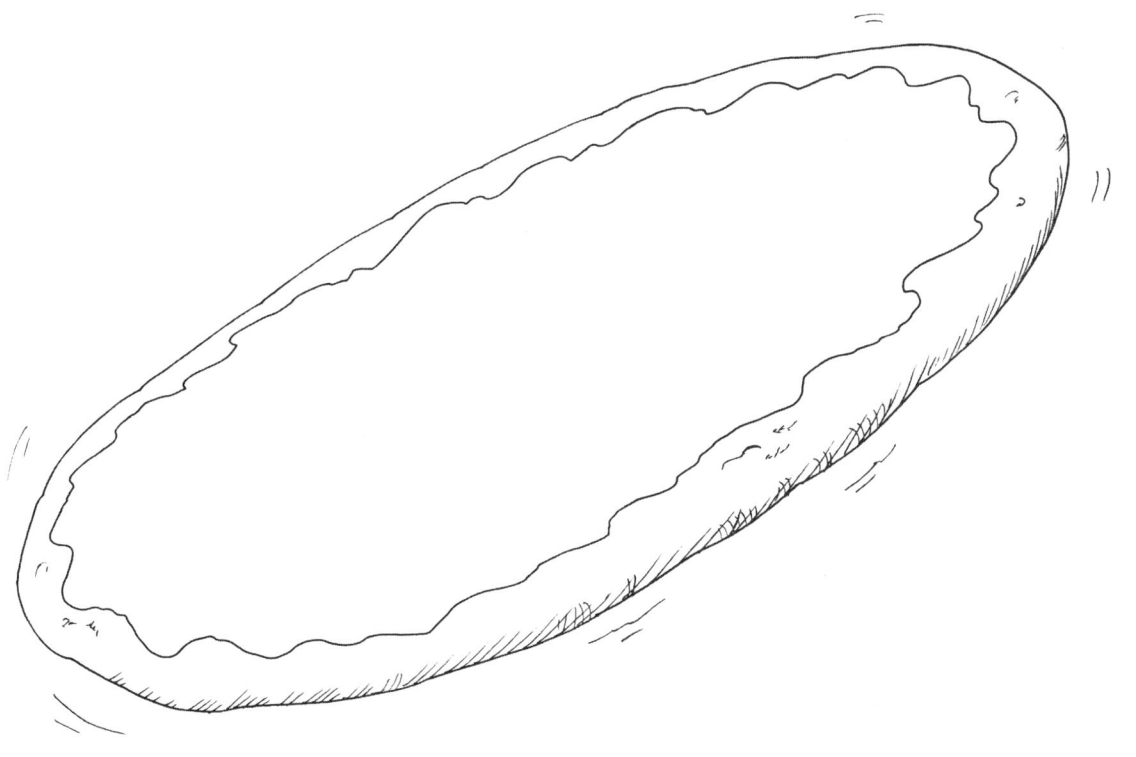

. . . and a disgusting one for someone else.

What's in the pyramid?

Design the scariest roller coaster ever.

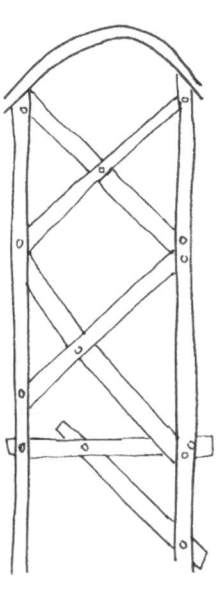

Save yourselves!

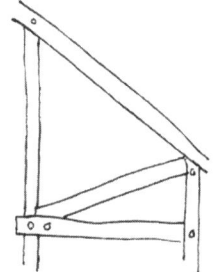

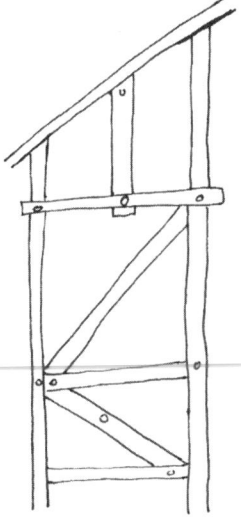

Who is bouncing?

Where are they going to land?

Not quite where I planned.

Invent a huge ice cream.

Why is he going bananas?

Who is next in the mud bath?

RESEARCHING YOUR FAMILY TREE

What is a family tree?

A family tree is a chart showing how all the members of a family are related. Everyone has a family tree – we all have a mum and a dad, and they have mums and dads too.

People who research family histories are called 'genealogists'. They talk to people and use historical records to gather information, and then they show it in a chart or write it down.

The shape of your tree will depend on the size of your family and how many generations you include. You'll be a genealogist too by the time you've completed this book!

Key words

❉ generation – members of a family treated as a single stage in the family tree.

❉ ancestor – a family member older than a grandparent.

❉ descendant – someone whose family can be traced back to a particular ancestor. For example, you are a descendant of your great-grandparents.

Be a busy bee and find out about your ancestors – it's great fun!

2

MY IRISH FAMILY TREE

How to create your family tree

Fill in the sections in this book. Ask your parents to help you find any information you need. Listen to stories from people in your family, find photographs and use the internet to help you. Once you have everything you need, start filling out your family tree.

Use these websites to help you:

http://kids.familytreemagazine.com/kids/

www.kidsturncentral.com/topics/hobbies/kidsgenealogy.htm

www.nli.ie/en/intro/family-history-introduction.aspx

www.irishtimes.com/ancestor/

Most Irish surnames have a history of their origin and a family crest. Go to www.irishsurnames.com and www.allfamilycrests.com to see if you can find yours.

Fitzgibbon   O'Connor
Diegan
Collins   Maloney

3

Where to look

Use these sources to help you with your research. Some can be found on the national archives website, www.nationalarchives.ie/

genealogy/sources.html

There are lots of ways to find out about your ancestors.

- Military records
- Property deeds
- Church records
- Passports
- Birth, marriage and death certificates

- Diaries and photographs
- Census records
- Land records
- Newspapers
- School records
- Workhouse records
- Obituaries and wills
- Ship passenger lists
- Medical records
- Transportation lists
- Emigration, immigration and nationalisation records

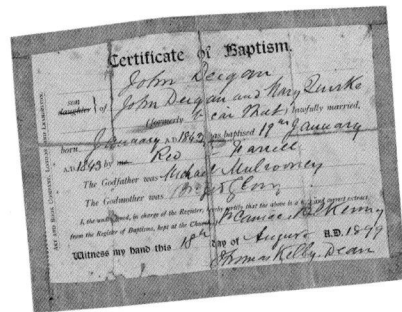

Census in Ireland

A census is an official survey of a country that records details about the population. Every five years a form is sent to every house in Ireland, filled in and collected.

Irish censuses from 1901 and 1911 are available free online. Go to www.census.nationalarchives.ie/ to search census records for information about your ancestors.

Where are they now?

Events in history caused lots of Irish people to emigrate (move abroad) in search of a better life. Between 1851 and 1921, three million people emigrated to America, Canada, Britain, Australia and New Zealand.

The Great Famine

The Great Famine (1845–50) was a major cause of emigration. Potato blight ruined crops and millions of people were left starving. Up to a million people died and many families were forced to emigrate.

Transportation

Between 1791 and 1853, thousands of convicts were sent to Australia and many people followed as free settlers. Search transportation lists for the names of your ancestors.

Go to www.nationalarchives.ie/genealogy/transportation.html

ALL ABOUT ME

Name: ....

Stick a photo or a drawing of yourself here

Me, as a baby

Date I was born:

....

Time I was born:

....

Stick a photo or a drawing of yourself here

Me, age...

Weight when
I was born: ....

Where I was born:

....

6

Who I live with:

....

....

Languages I speak:

....

....

....

Where I live now:

....

My school:

....

Ask your mum
and dad if you can see
your birth certificate.

Certificates & Achievements:

_____

_____

_____

_____

ABOUT MY MUM

Her name is: ....

Surname when she was born:

....

Where she was born:

....

Date she was born:

....

Where she lives now:

....

....

....

Stick a photo
or a drawing
of your
mum here

My mum, age...

Mum's age when I was born: ....

Number of siblings she has: ....

Languages she speaks: What she does:

....

....

....

Certificates & Achievements:

_____

_____

_____

_____

ABOUT MY DAD

His name is: ....

Where he was born:

....

Date he was born:

....

Stick a photo
or a drawing
of your
dad here

My dad, age...

Ask your dad
what games he liked to
play as a boy. Can you
find any pictures?

Where he lives now:

....

....

Dad's age when I was born: ....

Number of siblings he has: ....

Languages he speaks: What he does:

....

....

....

Certificates & Achievements:

_____

_____

_____

_____

ABOUT MY SIBLINGS

Number of
sisters I have:

....

Number of
brothers I have:

....

Siblings who live with me:

....

....

....

You may have half or step
brothers and sisters. If so,
write down how they are
related to you. For example,
'Tom is my half-brother.
We have the same mum.'

Name of my oldest sibling: ....

Date of birth:

....

Place of birth:

....

How they are related to me:

....

Things we like to do together:

....

....

Ask your brothers
or sisters what they like and
don't like. They
might surprise you!

Stick a photo
or a drawing
of your
sibling here

Name of my next oldest sibling:.............................

Date of birth:

....

Place of birth:

....

How they are related to me:

....

Things we like to do together:

....

Stick a photo
or a drawing
of your
sibling here

What are your
favourite memories of your
brothers and sisters?

Name of my next oldest sibling:.............................

Date of birth:

....

Place of birth:

....

Stick a photo
or a drawing
of your
sibling here

How they are related to me:

....

Things we like to do together:

....

If you have more than three brothers or
sisters then write their details on a piece
of paper and stick it to this page.

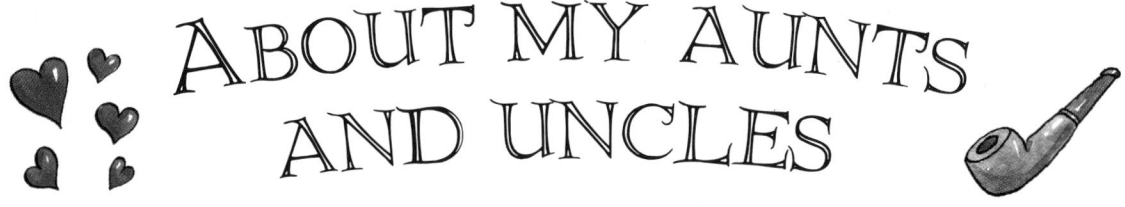

ABOUT MY AUNTS AND UNCLES

Your aunts and uncles are your
mum's and dad's brothers and sisters.

My mum's brothers and sisters:

Name: ....

Date of birth:

....

Place of birth:

....

Where he/she lives now:

....

Older or younger
than my mum?

....

Age difference:

....

Stick a photo
or a drawing
of your aunt or
uncle here

Name: ....

Date of birth: Age difference:

....

Place of birth:

....

Where he/she lives now:

Stick a photo
or a drawing
of your aunt
or uncle here

....

Older or younger
than my mum?

....

If your mum has more than two brothers
or sisters then write their details on a piece
of paper and stick it to this page.

My dad's brothers and sisters:

Name: ....

Date of birth: Age difference:

....

Place of birth:

....

Where he/she lives now:

....

Older or younger
than my dad?

....

Stick a photo
or a drawing
of your aunt or
uncle here

Name: ....

Date of birth: 🐝   **Age difference:**

....

Place of birth:

....

Where he/she lives now:

....

Older or younger than my dad?

Stick a photo or a drawing of your aunt or uncle here

....

If your dad has more than two brothers or sisters then write their details on a piece of paper and stick it to this page.

ABOUT MY COUSINS

Your cousins are the children of your mum's or dad's brothers and sisters. Ask your parents, or your aunts and uncles, to help you find out information about them.

My cousin's name:...

Date my cousin was born:

....

Where my cousin was born:

....

Where my cousin lives now:

....

Relation to me: (e.g. my mum's sister's son)

....

Stick a photo or a drawing of your cousin here

My cousin's name: ....

Date my cousin was born:

....

Where my cousin was born:

....

Where my cousin lives now:

....

Relation to me: (e.g. my mum's sister's son)

Stick a photo
or a drawing
of your
cousin here

....

....

Ask your cousins
what they like to do.
You might have some
things in common.

My cousin's name:..

Date my cousin was born:

....

Where my cousin was born:

....

Where my cousin lives now:

....

Relation to me: (e.g. my mum's sister's son)

....

....

Stick a photo or a drawing of your cousin here

Ask your parents if you have any second cousins too – these are your parents' cousins' children.

Favourite memories of my cousins:

....

....

If you have more than three cousins then write their
details on a piece of paper and stick it to the page.
Can you find out who all of your cousins are?

ABOUT MY GRANDPARENTS

Your grandparents are your mum's and dad's parents.

My mum's mum:

Her name:...

Her date of birth:

....

Where she was born:

....

Her job:

....

Stick a photo
or a drawing
of your mum's
mum here

My mum's dad:

His name: ....

His date of birth:

....

Where he was born:

....

His job:

....

Stick a
photo or a
drawing of
your mum's
dad here

Memories & Experiences:

_____

_____

_____

My dad's mum:

Her name: ....

Her date of birth:

....

Where she was born:

....

Her job:

....

Stick a photo
or a drawing
of your dad's
mum here

Memories & Experiences:

_____

_____

_____

My dad's dad:

His name: ....

His date of birth:

....

Where he was born:

....

His job:

....

Stick a
photo or a
drawing
of your dad's
dad here

Memories & Experiences:

_____

_____

_____

ABOUT MY GREAT-GRANDPARENTS

Your great-grandparents are your grandparents' parents. You have four sets of great-grandparents; two sets on your mum's side of the family and two on your dad's side. Can you find out about them all?

On my mum's side
My grandmother's mum and dad:

Grandmother's mum:.....................................

Her date of birth: Where she was born:

....

Grandmother's dad:.....................................

His date of birth: Where he was born:

....

28

My grandfather's mum and dad:

Grandfather's mum: ....

Her date of birth: Where she was born:

....

Grandfather's dad: ....

His date of birth: Where he was born:

....

My mum was a cook in a big house in Dublin. I loved her cooking when I was a girl.

My dad was a ship-builder in Waterford. I loved hearing about all the ships.

On my dad's side
My grandmother's mum and dad:

Her mum:..

Her date of birth: Where she was born:

....

Her dad:...

His date of birth: Where he was born:

....

Can you find some old photos of
your great-grandparents to stick
in? Don't forget to label who is
who. Can you find out how old
they were in each picture, and
what they did for a living?

My grandfather's mum and dad:

His mum:……………………………………………………………………

Her date of birth: Where she was born:

………………………………   ………………………………

His dad:……………………………………………………………………

His date of birth: Where he was born:

………………………………   ………………………………

Why not carry on your family tree further back than your great-grandparents? You might find out some exciting things!

Now it's time to fill in your family tree! Start with yourself and work upwards. The right-hand side is for your dad's family, and the left-hand side is for your mum's family.

Add your great-grandparents on the top row.

Add your grandparents here.

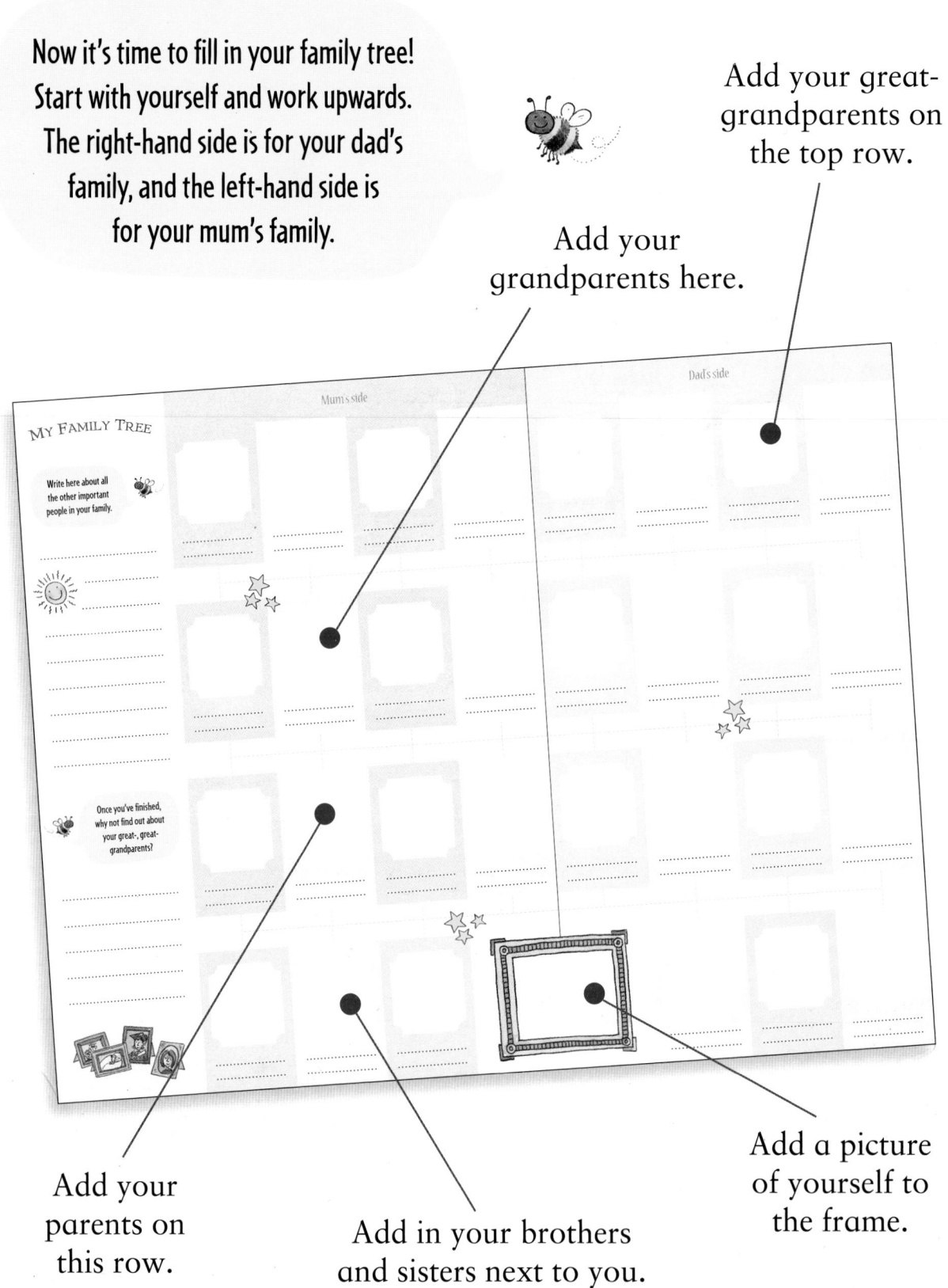

MY FAMILY TREE

Mum's side

Dad's side

Write here about all the other important people in your family.

Once you've finished, why not find out about your great-, great-grandparents?

Add your parents on this row.

Add in your brothers and sisters next to you.

Add a picture of yourself to the frame.

32